QUESTIONS TO ASK

Before You Say "I Do"

Evaluating Compatibility Before Becoming One

DAN D. JOHNSON

151 Questions to Ask Before You Say "I Do"
Evaluating Compatibility Before Becoming One

For more information contact:

www.shepublishingllc.com or
info@shepublsihingllc.com

Cover and Title Page Design by Michelle Phillips of
CHELLD3 3D VISUALIZATION AND DESIGN
ISBN: 978-1-953163-53-0

First Edition Revised: December 2022

DEDICATION

This book is dedicated to the readers.
May your decision of holy matrimony be filled with love, inspiration, information, and commitment.
May your "I do" transcend time into eternity and never end in "I don't."

CONTENTS

ACKNOWLEDGMENTS

To my wife, the inspiration by which this book was written. It is our relationship that gave birth to the wisdom of the pages that follow. thank you for a never-ending cycle of growth, development, and maturity in our time of marriage.

To my spiritual mother, Dr. Cindy Trimm, it is your impartation of wisdom, counsel, encouragement and guidance that has allowed this book to evolve from a concept to manifestation, thank you!

FOREWORD

It *is clear to me that although* men and women think differently and act differently, God has designated an institution in which two opposites can become a dynamic one. This God-ordained union is under fire, and Dan Johnson shares personal, practical principles to those seeking solutions to failing marriages, or those requiring fortification. There are many significant books on marriage but this one is a testimony of the literary genius of its author, and his ability to take on the contemporary issues and challenges this institution faces today.

We find ourselves in the greatest need to understand relationships especially within the confines of marriage. I know of no other book like this one. Although the topic of marriage is its main focus, it contains a practical outlook for both the married and the singles.

This is a book with its insightful twist, literary elegance and truth, gives us a deeper understanding of the complexities involved in building a strong and healthy relationship with the opposite sex.

Dan Johnson shares the personal with the practical as he presents revolutionary information with compassion, sensitivity and insight.

This is not just another manuscript on marriage & relationships. It is a motivational hand-book that will take you into new dimension of knowledge and give you a plan of action.

Dan Johnson is a spiritual son whom I have found to be a man of purpose, wisdom and insight way beyond his years. He is the next upcoming generational spiritual leader. I highly endorse and recommend the true words of wisdom you will find in the pages of this insightful book which focuses on one of the world's most intriguing subjects — the beautiful mystery of marriage. This book contains indispensable and metamorphic tools that will eventually become the marriage classic for future generations.

Ambassador Dr. N. Cindy Trimm

INTRODUCTION

M*arriage is:* • The state of being united to a person as husband or wife in a consensual and contractual relationship recognized by law • An intimate or close union • The joining of lives of two individuals with the intentions of those two lives becoming one • The merging of two individual mind-sets, back-grounds, personalities, and so forth, as a result of love expressed by those individuals and the belief that this love is eternal and will last through the test of time • Often the result of time spent in getting to know each other, the experiences of diverse emotions, the sharing of moments of joy and happiness, the expression of love and intimacy, as well as the communication of passion, in many cases, through sexual acts.

The wedding day is a time of celebration, happiness, the joining of two families, and the public declaration that the independent lives of two different people are becoming one. It is understood that as a result of this day, life brings a new beginning, a fresh start, new opportunities, and many years of love and happiness. After all, there is nothing more beautiful than the bride, while the groom glistens with satisfaction as his eyes behold what he now can call only his.

Almost every little girl's dream is to be desired and loved so much that a young man is willing to commit himself to taking care of her for the rest of her life. For a little boy, marriage is the point of assumed manhood. It means taking on the mandate of starting a family, and taking on the responsibility of providing a good life for that family. It is through the marriage union that life evolves, and generations of families are established.

The first marriage was instituted by God between Adam and Eve. Here we find a man who seemingly lived in paradise, whereby he had authority over everything in the earth, and had access to whatever he needed to live a fulfilled life. Yet the writing of Adam and Eve advises that God said he was alone. As a result of this void in loneliness, God gave him a wife named Eve.

The first purpose that God intended for marriage was companionship. Companionship is the fellowship existing among companions. It is a way to provide assistance and support to one another. Marriage creates a certain level of intimacy that causes individuals to become one. Eve was made for Adam to become a suitable helper, a woman that would complement and complete him in every way. In all of life's struggles, pain, and disappointment, you will need each other's companionship and intimacy. This intimacy develops from an attitude of servant hood in seeking to meet each other's needs and desires.

Irrespective of the fond memories of courtship, despite the joy filled with that special day, regardless of the confessions made at the altar, statistics show that 50% of all marriages end in divorce. How is it possible for so many "I dos" throughout the world to eventually end in "I don't"? What happened to the love that was so strong that by confession the only way separation was possible was through death? What happened to the passion that ran so deep that coming together was the highlight of the day and separating from one another was the darkness of night?

Individuals fall in love, believing it to be perfect and timeless, only to discover in time that the person who once seemed to fit every part of the other's life and dreams has opinions and habits and desires of their own. Those things don't fit, are not interesting, and eventually conflict with how life is supposed to look for the other. It seems that couples go from being soul mates to being incompatible almost overnight.

Lack of compatibility is a growing reason for divorce in marriages, often classified as irreconcilable differences. An old saying suggests that opposites attract. Unfortunately, this attraction may rapidly disappear as time goes on and the differences may separate the couple rather than bring them closer together. Exploring the compatibility that exists between individuals seeking to tie the knot does not guarantee a "happily ever after" marriage; however, it does allow aspiring couples to evaluate how much their compatibility or lack thereof affects the long-term standings of their marriage.

INTRODUCTORY QUESTIONS

Communication | The value of this book rests on the ability to communicate and discuss effectively, freely, honestly, and consistently how each other feels and views each question. Before we begin our series of 151 questions to ask before you say I do, below you would find introductory questions highlighting your method(s) of communication.

A. Would you consider yourself a communicator?

B. You and your partner have a disagreement on a passionate subject matter. Your partner would like to continue dealing with it right away; however, you would like to postpone it until a later time. How much time is considered a later time? If your partner persisted, how would you respond?

C. There is a conflict of views on a particular subject matter. How much time are you willing to discuss the matter before you feel that this subject should be concluded? Is there ever a time you would discontinue dialogue prior to resolving the conflict?

D. After identifying that something you may have said and/or did offend your partner, how flexible are you to hear their heart whether you agree or not, and then make certain adjustments to secure their feelings?

E. How much of your true feelings do you hold in for the sake of preserving the feelings of your partner?

F. Would you agree to honestly discuss each question identified in this book?

The purpose of this book is to provide a simple approach to assessing both the similarities and differences of individual views that would affect the collective union and cohesiveness of a marriage. Though there are a lot more questions that should be considered before saying “I do”, this book explores 151 of them that are designed to stimulate dialogue of marriage beyond love and throughout eternity.

This book is a designed to get couples to engage in dialogue about the various views, opinions, likes, dislikes, agreements, as well as disagreements that may or may not be discussed without a formal guide. It is recommended that:

1. Both parties answer all questions separately.

2. Once both parties have completed all the questions then both parties should come together and discuss each question together.

3. Document any disagreements on the blank page following each chapter.

4. Discuss the disagreement to determine if there is a line of compromise. If there is a compromise document it, if not notate it on your compromise page.

5. At the end of each chapter there is a scoring sheet divided into 4 categories

(a) Disagree

(b) Agree with compromise

(c) Agree and

(d) N/A, you should check the appropriate box for each question.

6. The highest total points is 285 points; points are earned according to level of compatibility. For example, disagree = 1 point, somewhat agree = 3 points, agree = 5 points and N/A = 0 points.

In identifying compatibility your total scores are divided into 5 categories:

0 – 80 points = don't do it, just be friends

81 – 138 points = reconsider marriage until both parties are able to receive an extended amount of counseling and can show a greater amount of agreement prior to getting married

139 – 196 points = proceed with caution, engage in 3rd party counseling

197 – 254 points = good match, keep an open line of communication

255 – 285 points = great match, congratulations on a new life.

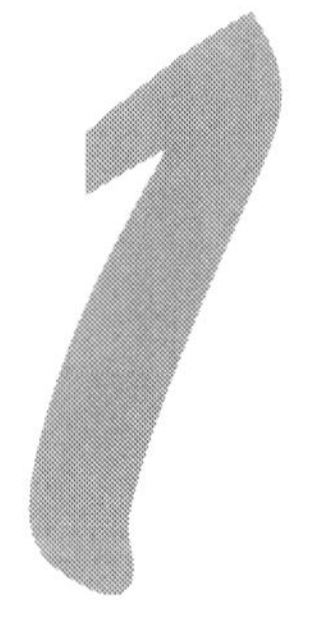

VISION & GOALS

Chapter 1

DEFINING VISION

The start of anything significant in life is vision.

Vision takes an individual beyond where they are and places them theoretically where they desire to be. Often times vision becomes the energy that drives an individual to succeed as well as governs and individuals thought process and patterns of behavior. In the context of marriage, more cases than none, both parties have an idea, concept or vision, by which they have for the marriage and their family. It is very important that early on this vision holds similarity from both parties' point of view. It is also necessary to discuss individual visions, for if there are major differences in the direction that each party are seeking to go, this too can cause complications in the marriage after the honeymoon stage. Having vision is essential as it allows you to develop a clear picture of your future and becomes the premise by goals are established.

IMPORTANCE OF GOALS

Goals are the tools that will be needed to help you reach your intended vision, minimizing unnecessary bumps in the roads as a result of not having a road map. Goal setting is a constant process of implementing strategies, actions, and time frames while pursuing a worthy objective until it's obtained. Goal setting is a powerful ongoing process for planning your future. The process for setting goals helps you determine where you desire to go in life. By knowing precisely what you want to achieve, you know where you have to concentrate your time, energy, and efforts. You will also be able to quickly identify distractions and obstacles that can potentially keep you off course. In addition, goal setting can be incredibly motivating, and as you develop a habit of setting and achieving goals, it can be a great self-confidence booster.

The primary purpose of goal setting is to help you organize your time and your resources so that you can make the most out of your life. By setting sharp, clearly defined goals, you can see forward progress in what might have been a pointless endeavor. Therefore, in setting your goals, you must first determine the goals that you want to set. Secondly, prioritize your goals in order of importance. Thirdly, set a five-year plan, one year plan, six-month plan, and a one-month plan. Lastly, create a daily to-do list of things you should do today to work toward your goals. Keep this process going by constantly reviewing and updating your to-do list on a daily basis.

In the questions to follow, you will begin to evaluate various areas of your life such as education/career, retirement, family/home, and recreation, and begin to get a clear vision of where you are currently and where you want to be in your future. Once you've answered the questions, you will have made a clear picture as to where you want to be. In doing so, you will be able to decide what is important for you to achieve in your life. You will also be able to separate what is relevant from what is irrelevant.

Education/Career | It is very important to understand your partner's educa- tional and professional ambitions and goals. Oftentimes, entrepreneurship, a demanding job, or continued education after marriage has a strong impact on the entire family. The time spent at work or needed to successfully finish school may cut into family time or vacation as a result of an overwhelming schedule. This section explores the overall vision and goal of your career choices and educational aspirations.

1. What is the highest level of education you seek to achieve?
2. Do you currently have a degree?
3. What is your preferred profession or career?
4. What do you currently do as a profession?
5. Are you inspired to be an entrepreneur?

Retirement | Understanding the retirement plans of your spouse is quite helpful in knowing expectations of savings, postretirement plans, and so forth. For example, if you or your partner seeks an early retirement, this decision will often require a greater sacrifice of savings and work on the front-end of your life so that one can work less or not at all during their retirement years. Time of retirement, in many cases, also affects the standard of living after retirement.

6. At what age do you seek to retire?
7. After retirement, what are your plans?
8. If the economy today mirrored the economy at the time of retirement, how much money do you think is needed to retire on?
9. When would you say you should start saving for retirement, and at what percentage of income?
10. Do you perceive yourself working the same job through retirement?

Family/Home | Everyone has an ideology of what family is supposed to be. There are many factors of your ideas that will affect the unity and compatibility between you and your partner. Your idea of family values will govern your expectations of how your home should be run. If your partner is not in agreement with your ideology of family, your house will be divided, and very likely your marriage will have many troubles.

11. How long after marriage would you like to have children?

12. How many children would you like to have?

13. How many days a week do you prefer a home cooked meal?

14. How important is it to you for family to eat meals together?

15. How many hours a week should the family have family time?

Recreation | Recreation is activities and experiences designed for pleasure, fun, and relaxation. Family recreation is often the time the entire family or simply you and your partner enjoy one another's presence, while creating a closer bond in the relationships that exist throughout the family. If interests of recreation are not similar, recreation time for one may not bring pleasure, fun, or relaxation, which could potentially cause the other not to enjoy them either. This will then limit recreation time in your home, as well as limit the quality of time spent with each other. The danger is that this opens the door for either partner to look outside the marriage for recreational companionship, which could lead to jealousy, division, and infidelity.

16. What are your hobbies?
17. Do you like to travel? Are you afraid of flying?
18. many times a year should the family takes vacations?
19. How often should just the husband and wife get away alone?
20. Describe a recreational evening with your partner. Describe a recreational evening with your family.

CHAPTER 1

Questions & Answers

1. What is the highest level of Education you seek to achieve?

____

____

____

____

2. Do you currently have a degree?

____

____

____

____

3. What is your preferred profession or career?

____

____

____

4. What do you currently do as a profession?

____

____

____

____

5. Are you inspired to be an entrepreneur?

____

____

____

____

6. At what age do you seek to retire?

____

____

____

____

____

____

____

7. After retirement, what are your plans?

____

____

____

____

8. If the economy today mirrored the time of retirement, how much money do you think is needed to retire on?

____

____

____

____

9. When would you say you should start saving for retirement, and at what percentage of income?

____

____

____

____

10. Do you perceive yourself working the same job through retirement?

____

____

____

____

11. How long after marriage would you like to have children?

____

____

____

12. How many children would you like to have?

____

____

____

____

____

____

13. How many days a week do you prefer a home cook meal?

____

____

____

____

____

____

14. How important is it to you for family to eat meals together?

____

____

____

____

____

____

____

15. How many hours a week should the family have family time?

16. What are your hobbies?

17. Do you like to travel? Are you afraid of flying?

18. How many times a year should the family takes vacation?

____

____

____

____

____

19. How often should just the husband and wife get away alone?

____

____

____

____

____

____

20. Describe a recreational evening with your spouse? Family?

____

____

____

____

____

____

____

Charting Your *Compatibility*

Chapter 1 Q&A Review	Agree (5 pts.)	Somewhat Agree (3 pts.)	Disagree (1 pt.)	N/A (0 pt.)
If the economy today mirrored the economy at the time of retirement, how much money do you think is needed to retire on?				
When would you say you should start saving for retirement, and at what percentage of income?				
How long after marriage would you like to have children?				
How many children would you like to have?				
How many days a week do you prefer a home cooked meal?				
How important is it to you for family to east meals together?				
How many hours a week should the family have family time?				
How many times a year should the				

family take a vacation?				
How often should just the husband and wife get away alone?				

Overall Combined Score ___________

IDENTIFYING
Compromise

Disagreement

Compromise

Disagreement

Compromise

Disagreement

____

____

____

____

____

____

____

____

Compromise

____

____

____

____

____

____

We hereby agree to disagree and adhere to the above written compromise in the areas of disagreement.

________________ ________________

Signature Signature

2 HISTORICAL BACKGROUND

Chapter 2

FAMILY HISTORY

Like it or not, marrying someone usually involves the formation of several relationships other than the husband-wife union. A person entering marriage automatically gains a father-in-law, a mother-in-law, sisters or brothers-in-laws, plus a variety of extended family members related to your new spouse. Although you don't technically marry the whole family, your relationship to your spouse may be largely affected by how well you get along with his/her family and even how well they get along with your family. Realistically, it is important to remember that your partner will likely reflect the values, attitudes, personality, and behaviors that you observe in his/her parent and grandparent generations.

GENERATIONAL TRAITS

Generational "traits" are inherited within families, and one of the mechanisms through which these are passed down is by emotional genetic patterns. These emotional genetic patterns serve as building blocks within each person's psyche. These patterns of could also be considered as precursors to specific emotional personality traits that may manifest in us.

Generational traits are distinguishing qualities or characteristics of a person. Traits are a readiness to think or act in a similar fashion in response to a variety of different stimuli or situations.

FAMILY VALUES

Family values are moral beliefs, attitudes, and personal preferences held to promote the sound functioning of the family and to strengthen the fabric of society. Family values are also principles that individuals consider to be right or important to the appropriate development of an individual or family unit. These principles include but are not limited to honesty and truthfulness, kindness, consideration, and concern for others, compassion, charity, humility, obedience, responsibility, and respect. These universal values build character, which produces behavior that is beneficial for the individual, others, and the community. They enhance the well-being of all, preventing harm to both the individual and society; and they are the essence of healthy relationships.

In the questions to follow, you will begin to evaluate your historical background and understand how your relationships with your parents, your belief system, and the good and bad things that have occurred in your life have impacted you. Additionally, you will learn how your values on educational and your chosen profession have had a major impact on developing your family values. In doing so, you will be able to determine how your values and that of your partner compare to one another.

Mother/Father | Getting to know the history of your potential partner's parents helps you understand some things you may be faced with in your marriage. In many sectors, these traits are considered to be generational or in the blood line of your partner. You should look at this history closely to evaluate certain patterns of behavior and potential belief systems, as well as problems that may possibly occur throughout the marriage.

21. Are/were your parents married? Did they get a divorce?
22. Are/were your parents faithful to each other?
23. How often did your parents argue?
24. Was either parent ever verbally, physically, or emotionally abusive either to you or the other parent? How did it affect you?
25. Was either one of your parents addicted to any controlled substance or alcohol?

Belief System on Family | How or what one believes will govern their thought process, determine their speech, and dictate their behavior. It is critically important that two individuals seeking to become one share the same belief systems. A house divided against itself cannot stand.

26. How often do you feel the extended family

(aunts, uncles, cousins, etc.) should get together?

27. How do you feel about giving children spankings as a form of discipline?

28. How much television should a child watch each week?

29. How do you feel about family prayer time?

30. If your partner felt that the family should change religions or home school your children, how would you respond?

Memorable Things (Good and Bad) | The Events that have taken place in our past can easily affect how we deal with our future. When negative or "bad" things happen, if those things are not properly handled or dealt with, it can cause problems in relationships later. Individuals should be very open and honest about their past. This allows the other to understand some behaviors that may exist as a result of your past. It also allows him or her to be more sensitive to certain situations that may remind one of the "bad" things. Communication about your past can solve problems in your future before they exist.

31. What was the most exciting thing that happened to you as a child?

32. What was the worst thing that ever happened to you as a child?

33. Have you ever been abused in any way?

34. While growing up, what was the most memorable moment with your family?

35. How did you respond to both the good and bad moments? Have there been any longterm effects? Explain.

Educational/Profession | Here again, we are given some kind of insight as to the educational and professional status and your spouse aspires, by evaluating that of his or her family background. Although not always, there are times the status of higher education and employment in a family's background will determine that of your potential partner's. This is so important as if you seek a higher education and economic status than your partner's, there will be an intellectual disparity, and possibly a vast disparity from one income to the other. This may or may not cause problems based on how each individual views the household income.

This also usually affects the taste buds and spending habits of both parties.

36. What was the highest achieved education from your mother and father?
37. What industry did your mother and/or father work in?
38. Did both parents work? If not, which one stayed at home?
39. What was your parent(s) average household income?
40. Was either parent an entrepreneur? How did this impact the family? What is your view on entrepreneurship?

CHAPTER 2

Questions & Answers

21. Are/were your parents married? Did they get a divorce?

____

____

____

____

____

____

22. Are/were your parents faithful to each other?

____

____

____

____

____

____

23. How often did your parents argue?

____

____

____

____

____

____

24. Was either parent verbally, physically, or emotionally abusive?

____

____

____

____

____

____

25. Was either one of your parents addicted to any controlled substance or alcohol?

____

____

____

____

____

____

____

26. How often do you feel the extended family (aunts, uncles, cousins, etc.) should get together?

____

____

____

____

____

____

27. How do you feel about giving children spankings as a form of discipline?

____

____

____

____

____

____

28. How much television should a child watch each week?

____

____

____

____

____

____

____

29. How do you feel about family prayer time?

____

____

____

____

____

____

30. If your partner felt that the family should change religions or home school your children, how would you respond?

____

____

____

____

____

____

31. What was the most exciting thing that happened to you as a child?

____

____

____

____

____

____

32. What was the worst thing that ever happened to you as a child?

____

____

____

____

____

____

33. Have you ever been abused in any way?

____

____

____

____

____

____

34. While growing up, what was the most memorable moment with your family?

____

____

____

____

____

____

____

35. How did you respond to both the good and bad moments? Have there been any long-term effects?

36. What was the highest achieved education from your mother and father?

37. What industry did your mother and/or father work in?

38. Did both your parents work? If not, which one stayed at home?

39. What was your parent(s) average household income?

40. Was either parent an entrepreneur?

Charting Your *Compatibility*

Chapter 2 Q&A Review	Agree (5 pts.)	Somewhat Agree (3 pts.)	Disagree (1 pt.)	N/A (0 pt.)
How often do you feel the extended family (aunts, uncles, cousins, etc.) should get together?				
How do you feel about giving children spankings as a form of discipline?				
How much television should a child watch each week?				
How do you feel about family prayer time?				
If your partner felt that the family should change religions or home school your children, how would you respond?				
How many hours a week should the family have family time?				
How many times a year should the family take vacations?				
How often should just the husband and wife get away alone?				

Overall Combined Score ___________

IDENTIFYING
Compromise

Disagreement

Compromise

Disagreement

Compromise

Disagreement

____

____

____

____

____

____

____

____

Compromise

____

____

____

____

____

____

We hereby agree to disagree and adhere to the above written compromise in the areas of disagreement.

____________________ ____________________

Signature Signature

3 SPIRITUAL WALK

Chapter 3

UNEQUALLY YOKED

While you examine your relationship; it is important to recognize if you and your partner are equally yoked together. Many times, individuals find themselves spiritually connected to others that share a distinctly different view on their spiritual from yours. Their morals, values and perceptions of life are far different from what we believe. When two people are joined together, it is important to determine if the relationship is built on mutually solid spiritual foundation. When two individuals come together naturally but are not spiritually compatible, starting a marriage with such disparity will only lead to problems.

To further explain, if a donkey and an ox are yoked together, the yoke will weigh heavily on one animal while choking the other, or as the animal with the longer stride moves ahead, it will painfully drag the other along by the neck! They would not be able to pull smoothly or painlessly together and little work would get done. But when two animals of approximately the same size and weight are yoked together, they pull the plow smoothly, helping each other; therefore, work is accomplished. Becoming attached to a person who does not share your faith can be just as painful and counterproductive as the illustration of the unequally yoked animals.

In the questions to follow, we will begin to evaluate your spiritual walk regarding your statement of belief, study and prayer life, your worship experience, and your faith walk. These questions were designed to identify where you are in your spiritual walk and to even consider where you desire to be as you mature spiritually. In making this determination, you will be able to recognize if you and your partner are moving in the same direction.

Statements of Beliefs | There are many religions, denominations, and spiritual organizations that serve as the governing authority of one's values, moral code of ethics, and even life. Exploring the foundation of your partner's religious beliefs, if any, can immediately determine whether or not marriage is an option. Though many try, it is very difficult for two individuals with different religious beliefs to have a successful marriage.

41. What denomination of church, if any, are you a part of?

42. Do you believe in Christian theology? If no, please advise.

43. What is your view on God?

44. What holidays do you observe?

45. Is God, your religious beliefs, the governing force in your life?

Study and Prayer Life | Once agreement has been established in what both parties would believe, equal development of this belief, as well as an understanding how the union would practice this belief is also necessary. Again, living by the same governing message, reading the same kind of material, and praying similar prayers would assist in the unity and synchronization of the entire household. As a people, what we allow to go into our eye gates (what we see) and ear gates (what we here), ultimately fashions our behavior.

46. Do you believe in maintaining a consistent prayer life?

47. How often do you read your Bible, Koran, or religious works by which you govern your life?

48. Do you pray in tongues, chants, or any other spiritual language other than English?

49. How important is it to you to teach your children how to pray and study? Should the decision be that of the child?

50. Do you believe in fasting? How often? Do you expect your partner to fast with you?

Worship Experience | though the foundational religious beliefs are the same, desire or opinion in how this belief is expressed can be different. Understanding these views and desires ahead of time allows individuals to determine the true compatibility of their spiritual walks.

51. How often do you attend some kind of worship or religious service each week?

52. How do you feel about gospel and/or Christian music?

53. Do you feel attending church is a core focus of your family activity?

54. Do you believe that both the husband and wife should attend religious activities together?

55. Are you opposed to female leadership in religious sectors?

Faith Walk | Faith is the belief in something that may not be seen and/or understood by logical minds of an opposing society. Faith causes individuals to act based on what they believe opposed to what their society suggests makes sense. Some decisions are made based on faith, it is essential that both parties understand each other's degree and level of faith. Otherwise, situations will occur that have the ability to cause major disagreements in the marriage; one is operating by what they have called faith, while the other thinks this behavior is foolish.

56. What is your definition of faith?

57. What percentage of your decisions is based upon faith?

58. Do you believe in miracles?

59. Have you ever seen faith in action?

60. Is there anything that faith cannot handle?

CHAPTER 3

Questions & Answers

41. What denomination of church, if any, are you a part of?

42. Do you believe in Christian theology? If no, please advise.

43. What is your view on God?

44. What holidays do you observe?

45. Is God the governing force in your life?

46. Do you believe in maintaining a consistent prayer life?

47. How often do you read your Bible, Koran, or religious works by which you govern your life?

48. Do you pray in any language other than English?

49. How important is it to you to teach your children how to pray and study? Should the decision be that of the child?

____

____

____

____

____

____

50. Do you believe in fasting? How often? Do expect your partner to fast with you?

____

____

____

____

____

____

51. How often do you attend some kind of worship or religious service each week?

____

____

____

____

____

____

52. How do you feel about gospel and/or Christian music?

____

53. Do you feel attending church is a core focus of you family activity?

54. Do you believe that both the husband and wife should attend religious activities together?

55. Are you opposed to female leadership in religious sectors?

56. What is your definition of faith?

57. What percentage of your decisions are based upon faith?

58. Do you believe in miracles?

59. Have you ever seen faith in action?

60. Is there anything that faith cannot handle?

Charting Your *Compatibility*

Chapter 3 Q&A Review	Agree (5 pts.)	Somewhat Agree (3 pts.)	Disagree (1 pt.)	N/A (0 pt.)
What denomination of church, if any, are you a part of?				
Do you believe in Christian theology?				
What is your view on God?				
What holidays do you observe?				
Is God the governing force in your life?				
Do you believe in maintaining a consistent prayer life?				
How important is it to you to teach your children how to pray and study? Should the decision be that of the child?				
Do you believe in fasting? How often? Do you expect your partner to fast with you?				
How often do you attend some kind of worship or religious service each week?				
Do you feel attending church is a core focus				

of your family activity?				
Do you believe that both the husband and the wife should attend religious activities together?				
Are you opposed to female leadership in religious sectors?				

Overall Combined Score __________

IDENTIFYING
Compromise

Disagreement

Compromise

Disagreement

Compromise

Disagreement

Compromise

We hereby agree to disagree and adhere to the above written compromise in the areas of disagreement.

Signature Signature

ROLE OF FINANCES

Money is a medium of exchange that is widely accepted in payment for goods and services and in settlement of debts. Money also serves as a standard of value for measuring the relative worth of different goods and services. Few couples, especially in the early years of marriage, are independently wealthy. This makes understanding how the finances will be handled within the marriage critical. Though household finances are a very in-depth discussion, this section seeks to examine some key things to consider. These questions only represent a few entities that will confront the marriage early on. According to marriage counselors, conflict over money is one of the primary reasons given by couples for seeking professional help. Serious conflict may be avoided if attitudes and philosophies about finances are clearly communicated prior to marriage, and continually during the marriage.

Marriage is as much a financial partnership as a union of hearts and minds. Nevertheless, getting that partnership to work well takes effort. The first step is to discuss your expectations about how money should be handled. Money can be a source of stress for most couples and it can be a catalyst for divorce. But a big difference between people who stay together and those who split is how they manage conflicts in their relationships.

DILEMMA WITH FINANCES

One of the dilemmas with finances is that there is often an uncertainty as to what creditors are owed and how much they are owed. The uncertainty in this area is a direct result of a lack of communication about finances and how finances should be clearly handled. Having and keeping a budget is often an area that is overlooked. However, having a budget has its benefits to the financial well being of your overall finances. A budget will help you in determining if you can really afford an item that you desire to purchase. It also makes you more conscious of your spending habits.

When it comes to finances, many people have different philosophies. If you're young, at times you may feel that it's too early to save for your future. On the other hand, an older person may wish that they would have started saving sooner. The question that follows explores areas that should be evaluated entering into marriage.

Joint Accounts | Finances are always a touchy subject in terms of marriage. One of the biggest topics is determining how and who is going to handle the household finances. The second question is a question of two individual incomes becoming one. Identifying early on whether or not joint accounts will be established, assessing if finances will be combined, and determining equal access and control regardless of whether or not there is a primary breadwinner, will assist in minimizing a lack of trust and many arguments about money in the future.

61. Do you believe married couples should have joint bank accounts?

62. Do you feel that couples should also have

separate bank accounts?

63. Is there ever a time where money you specifically made by your own efforts should be solely your money?

64. How do you feel about asking someone else how you can spend money you have earned?

65. Should you have a certain amount of money somewhere hidden that your partner does not know about?

Savings/Investments | Savings and investments play an integral part of the future and stability of the family. While everyone will agree to its importance, there is much disagreement with how these goals are achieved. This section helps identify the saving and investment habits of each other. The challenge in this aspect of the marriage lies in how saving and investment habits affect the current lifestyle and standard of living for the sake of saving for the future.

66. What percentage of your net household income should be set aside for savings?

67. Are you an aggressive or moderate investor?

68. Would you ever be willing to invest in a new

venture with uncertain returns?

69. What vehicle would you most comfortably want to save, a savings account, CD, money market, etc.?

70. What situation would you think is acceptable to go into the family savings for a non-emergency cause?

Budgeting | Budgeting is not the priority, nor a necessity for some individuals. However, for others a budget is the financial bible by which they live. If there is no agreement on whether or not a budget will be followed, or if either party decides an agreed upon budget is not that important and compromise it by overspending, then financial division and economic instability will be the end result.

71. Do you currently work from a budget?

72. Are you disciplined enough to maintain a budget?

73. Approximately how much should be budgeted for individual spending allowance after all bills are paid on a weekly or biweekly basis?

74. Who do you feel should handle the finances? You, your partner, or both?

75. On what occasion would you think it is appropriate to exceed your monthly budget?

Spending Priorities | Defining spending priorities also is as equally important in terms of establishing a budget. Oftentimes what may be needed for one might be less significant for others. For example, some may suggest, any bill that affects credit should be of the utmost importance; nevertheless, someone else may think utilities carry a greater weight.

76. In your opinion, what are the most important five bills that must be paid on time no matter what?

77. Do you feel that giving to charitable organizations or to those in need a priority?

78. A utility bill is due; however, there is not enough money to pay that bill, and purchase a new outfit, etc. Which do you pay?

79. Do you consider paying a tithe (10% of income) to your local church a priority? How a about a weekly offering?

80. Is there ever a time that vacation should be sacrificed for the sake of paying reoccurring bills?

CHAPTER 4

Questions & Answers

61. Do you believe married couples should have joint bank accounts?

62. Do you feel that couples should also have separate bank accounts?

63. Is there ever a time where money you specifically made by your own efforts should be solely your money?

64. How do you feel about asking someone else how you can spend money you have earned?

65. Should you have a certain amount of money somewhere hidden that your partner does not know about?

66. What percentage of your net household income should be set aside for savings?

67. Are you an aggressive or moderate investor?

68. Would you ever be willing to invest in a venture with uncertain returns?

69. What vehicle would you most comfortably want to save your money, a savings account, CD, money market, etc?

70. What situation would you think is acceptable to go into the family savings?

71. Do you currently work from a budget?

72. Are you disciplined enough to maintain a budget?

73. Approximately how much should be budgeted for individual spending allowance after all bills are paid on a weekly or biweekly basis?

____

____

____

____

____

74. Who do you feel should handle the finances? You, your partner, or both?

____

____

____

____

____

75. On what occasion would you think it is appropriate to exceed your monthly budget?

____

____

____

____

____

____

____

76. In your opinion, what are the most important five bills that must be paid no matter what?

____

____

____

____

____

____

77. What bills do you feel you can float and not pay on time, if any?

____

____

____

____

____

____

78. A utility bill is due; however, there is not enough money to pay that bill, and purchase a new outfit, etc. Which do you pay?

____

____

____

____

____

79. Do you consider paying a tithe (10% of income) a priority?

____

____

____

____

____

____

80. Is there ever a time that vacation should be sacrificed for the sake of paying reoccurring bills?

____

____

____

____

____

____

Charting Your *Compatibility*

Chapter 4 Q&A Review	Agree (5 pts.)	Somewhat Agree (3 pts.)	Disagree (1 pt.)	N/A (0 pt.)
Do you believe married couples should have joint bank accounts?				
Do you believe married couples should have separate bank accounts?				
Is there ever a time where money you specifically made by your own efforts should be solely your money?				
Should you have a certain amount of money somewhere hidden that your partner does not know about?				
What percentage of your net household income should be set aside for savings?				
Would you ever be willing to invest in a venture with uncertain returns?				
What vehicle would you most comfortably want to save your money, a savings account, CD, money market, etc?				
What situation would you think is acceptable to go into the family savings?				

Do you currently work from a budget?				
Are you disciplined enough to maintain a budget?				
Approximately how much should be budgeted for individual spending allowance after all bills are paid on a weekly or bi-weekly basis?				
Who do you feel should handle the finances? You, your partner, or both?				
On what occasion would you think it is appropriate to exceed your monthly budget?				
In your opinion, what are the most important five bills that must be paid no matter what?				
What bills do you feel you can float and not pay on time, if any?				
A utility bill is due; however, there is not enough money to pay that bill, and purchase a new outfit, etc. Which do you pay?				
Do you consider paying a tithe (10% of income) a priority?				
Is there ever a time that vacation should be sacrificed for the sake of paying reoccurring bills?				

Overall Combined Score ___________

IDENTIFYING
Compromise

Disagreement

Compromise

Disagreement

Compromise

Disagreement

____

____

____

____

____

____

____

____

Compromise

____

____

____

____

____

____

We hereby agree to disagree and adhere to the above written compromise in the areas of disagreement.

____________________ ____________________

Signature Signature

5 SEXUAL BACKGROUND & PREFERENCES

Chapter 5

ROLE OF SEX

Sex was created for physical enjoyment, more intimate bonding, and for procreation. Sex was created as a love expression between married couples for pleasure. Sex, for the marriage union is intended for them to be pleased at the very sight of their nakedness. There is also a spiritual bonding that takes place between two people that engage in sex. For the married, it is a renewal of the covenant of their matrimony and the blessings it attracts.

DILEMMA WITH SEX IN MARRIAGE

Sexual attraction plays a major part in bringing two people together and leading them to the altar of holy matrimony. A major component of continued satisfaction in marriage is a quality sexual relationship. A mutually satisfying sexual relationship, however, does not just happen automatically. As with other aspects of personality, a partner's sexuality is individual. Each person should approach the sexual relationship with respect and understanding for the other. As with other areas of marriage, sexual relations are interrelated, meaning that conflict or intense concern over money, for example, can detract from sexual interest.

Each partner may have different ideas about what is "right" and what is "wrong" in their sex life. In reality, there are no "rights" or "wrongs" in sexual activity between a married couple more so, what each may believe to be acceptable or unacceptable behavior. Personal beliefs should be honored and respected. Only you and your partner should decide what is acceptable and satisfying for the two of you. Don't try to fit your relationship into someone else's idea of what is "normal" sexual behavior.

Continue to learn more about your partner and about specific sex techniques. Some make sex a weapon in dealing with other conflicts in their relationship. Doing so magnifies the original problem, and can lead to sexual problems as well. As with other issues in the partnership, a satisfying sex life depends a great deal on open channels of communication. Don't be afraid to discuss your sex life with your partner. Share with him or her likes, dislikes, sexual beliefs, sexual history, and your preferences. Share and learn together. This section will show you how.

Sexual Beliefs | Sexual intimacy is a vital part of the marriage. Many would argue that it is one of the top reasons for divorce. Knowing the sexual beliefs ahead of time could help individuals determine their sexual compatibility.

81. Do you believe in multiple positions?

82. Do you believe in anal sex?

83. Do you believe in oral sex?

84. Do you believe in threesomes or foursomes?

85. Do you believe in swinging?

Sexual History | History is our greatest teacher. Examining the sexual experience and history clearly helps identify any information about your partner's past that could affect you and the relationship.

86. How many sex partners have you had?

87. Have you ever tested positive for STDs?

88. Have you ever been tested for HIV?

89. Have you ever engaged in homosexual activity?

90. Have you ever had multiple partners at one time?

Sexual Preferences | In light of sex, it is not safe to assume that equal love for one another translates into equality in sexual activity. The truth is that sex preferences among individuals can be very different, and can destroy a marriage if either individual needs are not being met.

91. How many times a week do you feel you need to have sex?

92. What percentage of your sexual experience is mental and emotional? What percentage is actually

the act of sex?

93. How do you feel about being totally nude in front of your partner? Do you like talking while having sex?

94. Does watching or reading pornography play a significant role in how you view sex?

95. How do you feel about engaging in sexual activity during your partner's or your menstrual cycle?

Sex and Communications | Communication in marriage overall is essential for a successful union. Communication in matters concerning sex is no exception. Each partner will be faced with the daunting task of expressing pleasure or the lack thereof to the other. This expression is to either encourage or highlight areas of improvement. Either way, feelings must be expressed and adjustments must be made in order to maintain a healthy, honest sex life.

96. There are moments where your partner may request an act that you are not in agreement with. How open-minded are you as it pertains to doing it anyway for the sake of satisfying your mate?

97. When your partner is having trouble pleasing

you, are you comfortable enough to advise your partner of their shortcoming?

98. Are you comfortable talking about sex freely enough to assist your partner in assuring your satisfaction?

99. You and your partner had a heated discussion; afterward, your partner decides to engage in sexual intimacy. How would you respond?

100. How important is foreplay to your overall sexual satisfaction?

CHAPTER 5

Questions & Answers

81. Do you believe in multiple positions?

82. Do you believe in anal sex?

83. Do you believe in oral sex?

84. Do you believe in threesomes or foursomes?

85. Do you believe in swinging?

86. How many sex partners have you had?

87. Have you ever been tested positive for STD's?

88. Have you ever been tested positive for HIV?

89. Have you ever engaged in homosexual activity?

90. Have you ever had multiple partners at one time?

91 How many times a week do you feel you need to have sex?

92. What percentage of your sexual experience is mental and emotional? What percentage is actually the act of sex?

93. How do you feel about being totally nude in front of your partner? Do you like talking while having sex?

94. Does watching or reading pornography play a significant role in how you view sex?

95. How do you feel about the usage of sex toys with your partner?

96. There are moments when your partner may request an act that you are not in agreement with. How open-minded are you as it pertains to doing it anyway for the sake of satisfying your mate?

97. When your partner is having trouble pleasing you, are you comfortable enough to advise your partner of their shortcomings?

____

____

____

____

____

98. Are you comfortable talking about sex freely enough to assist your partner in assuring your satisfaction?

____

____

____

____

____

99. You and your partner had a heated discussion; afterward, your partner decides to engage in sexual intimacy. How would you respond?

____

____

____

____

____

____

100. How important is foreplay to your overall sexual satisfaction?

____

____

____

____

____

____

Charting Your *Compatibility*

Chapter 5 Q&A Review	Agree (5 pts.)	Somewhat Agree (3 pts.)	Disagree (1 pt.)	N/A (0 pt.)
Do you believe in multiple positions?				
Do you believe in anal sex?				
Do you believe in oral sex?				
Do you believe in threesomes or foursomes?				
Do you believe in swinging?				
How many times a week do you feel you need to have sex?				
How do you feel about being totally nude in front of your partner? Do you like talking while having sex?				
Does watching or reading pornography play a significant role in how you view sex?				
How do you feel about the usage of sex toys with your partner?				
There are moments where your partner may request an act that you are not in agreement with.				

How open-minded are you as it pertains to doing it anyway for the sake of satisfying your mate?				
When your partner is having trouble pleasing you, are you comfortable enough to advise your partner of their shortcoming?				
Are you comfortable talking about sex freely enough to assist your partner in assuring your satisfaction?				
How important is foreplay to your overall sexual satisfaction?				

Overall Combined Score ___________

IDENTIFYING
Compromise

Disagreement

Compromise

Disagreement

Compromise

Disagreement

____

____

____

____

____

____

____

____

Compromise

____

____

____

____

____

____

We hereby agree to disagree and adhere to the above written compromise in the areas of disagreement.

____________________ ____________________

Signature Signature

6 THE NEXT 50 QUESTIONS THAT MATTERS

Chapter 6

According to Miles Mason Family Law Group, the Divorce rate in America, as of 2022, is approximately 44%-51%. There are many factors to contribute to this staggering statistic. We are living in a society where the tradition of two people finding love, getting married, and living happily ever after is not necessarily the norm. We are living in a time of blended families which involves having to engage ex partners due to having children from that previous relationship. We are living in a time of public sexual liberties and explorations that now requires a more detailed conversation of expectations; and we are living in a time where parenting styles and belief systems vary from one person to another. How you relate and/or engage in of all these dynamics MATTER!

As you go through life as a spouse, you grow through marriage. During that time of growth there will be many opportunities and challenges that you will face along the way. There are various matters that life will present that could potentially catch you off guard. Being prepared for the unexpected, and having some sense of understanding as to how you would respond is critically important.

This final chapter of questions deals with matters associated with the various social and practical belief systems that ultimately governs your marriage, having a blended family and dealing with the EX, and the exploration of both parties' sexual apetite to assure there is true compatibility and understanding. This chapter create an opportunity for evaluation, perspective, and ultimately honest dialogue as to how your partner would respond in respect to these important matters.

Family Matters

101. Do you believe in gender roles in a relationship? If so, what are they?

102. How do you feel about marriage counseling?

103. If the marriage counselor advises on something you disagree with, Will you adhere to it an anyway or disregard it?

104. What are your thoughts on abortion?

105. What are your political views?

106. How do u feel about your spouse parents living with you?

107. What would be your response if your child believes they are homosexual or desire to be a transgender?

108. How would you handle one of the children getting pregnant in high school?

109. In the event natural childbirth is difficult or impossible, how do you feel about adoption?

110. How would you handle if your partner gets addicted to alcohol, or illicit drugs or prescription drugs?

111. How do you handle your spouse becoming terminally ill early on in your marriage? Do you believe you can be caretaker for the long haul?

112. In life tragedy happens, the key to overcoming the tragedy is based on how you respond. How do you typically handle traumatic experiences?

113. Would you consider yourself a jealous person? How does jealousy affect your communication, attitude and interaction within your overall character in the relationship?

114. How do you feel about your spouse going out for a social evening without you? How often would you feel is acceptable?

115. One loves to travel, the other does not, are you comfortable with your partner traveling on guy trips or girl trips without you?

116. How important is the weight and physical appearance of your mate to you over the long term of your relationship?

117. How would you respond to your spouse if you feel

their form of discipline is abusive?

118. How do you feel about your spouse making personal large purchases in your name and on your credit?

119. What is your credit score?

120. Mental illness is a part of our lives, Do you believe that you will be able to stand by your partner that is diagnosed with a mental illness like schizophrenia or bipolar, and refuses medication?

121. Holidays are coming, what is your preference? A quiet time at home with your immediate family, a big gathering at your home with an open invite, or house hopping to various family and friends gathering?

122. The tax season could become a very stressful season in a marriage, there are various ways to file, some will allow greater returns than others, but may not be the most ethical. How would you prefer to file taxes as a married couple?

Ex Matters

123. Do you believe it's ok to have a close friend of the opposite sex?

124. Do you believe it's ok to maintain a relationship with your ex?

125. If your marriage will create a blended family, how important is it for you to have a relationship with your spouse's ex?

126. In a blended family, do you believe the non-organic parent should be allowed to physically discipline the child(ren) from the EX-partner?

127. Marriage comes with a lot of stress; loss of employment or income can happen. How well do you handle stress, for example, having to support the household as a result of your spouse losing their job, and your source of income is not enough?

128. How do u handle a partner that has an addiction to gambling, porn, or becomes a pedophile or a thief?

129. Unfortunately, divorce is a part of life which often times creates blended families. As a result, interactions with an EX may be necessary for the sake of the children. How would you respond with a difficult EX that creates chaos in the process?

130. Do you or your mate have to pay child support or alimony as a result of a previous relationship? If so,

do you feel this should be a joint expense or an expense for the person responsible for the child support?

131. If your potential partner already has children from a previous relationship and they opted to live with you, would you be in agreement? Explain why or why not?

132. What are your thoughts on allowing your former partner to have keys or access to your home just in case an emergency?

133. Do you believe your ex should be a beneficiary of your life insurance policy if you have children together?

134. You have a blended family, your spouse and his/or ex have a decent co-parenting relationship, your partner's ex is a very good cook and send your partner a plate or their favorite dessert for the Holidays, there is no interaction with the ex directly, only through the children. Are you ok with this?

135. In a blended family with smaller children from the previous relationship, are you comfortable with your spouse buying gifts "from the children" to give to your EX?

Sex Matters

136. Does Size Matter, if so, what's enough for you?
137. How easily are you to ejaculate, (On demand or requires a lot of work)
138. Are you a sensual person?
139. Do you think it's important to shower before having sex?
140. Your partner has gained weight over the years, you are not physically or sexually attracted to them at this current weight, do you tell them or just accept it and fake it?
141. What are your thoughts about having an open relationship with other couples (swinging)?
142. How do you feel about having an open marriage?
143. How do you feel about the usage of sex toys with your partner?
144. How important is affection and non-verbal communication to you?
145. What is your sexual fantasy?

146. Do you like public display of affection?

147. How do you think you would respond to being informed by your partner that they have been infected by an STD?

148. What is your favorite time of day to have sex? If your partner enjoys morning sex, and you are not a morning person, how do you respond?

149. The relationship is not going well, you do not desire to have sex with your partner, however, you do not want to separate, your partner has a sexual appetite and still have needs, they go outside of the marriage to get them met. Who's to blame?

CHAPTER 6

Questions & Answers

101. Do you believe in gender roles in a relationship? If so, what are they?

102. How do you feel about marriage counseling?

103. If the marriage counselor advises on something you disagree with, Will you adhere to it an anyway or disregard it?

____

____

____

____

____

104. What are your thoughts on abortion?

____

____

____

____

____

105. What are your political views?

____

____

____

____

____

____

____

____

____

106. How do u feel about your spouse parents living with you?

____

____

____

____

____

107. What would be your response if your child believes they are homosexual or desire to be a transgender?

____

____

____

____

____

108. How would you handle one of the children getting pregnant in high school?

____

____

____

____

____

____

____

____

109. Natural childbirth is difficult or impossible, how do you feel about adoption?

____

____

____

____

____

110. How would you handle if one partner gets addicted to alcohol, or illicit drugs or prescription drugs?

____

____

____

____

____

111. How do you handle your spouse becoming terminally ill early on in your marriage? Do you believe you can be caretaker for the long haul?

____

____

____

____

____

____

____

112. In life tragedy happens, the key to overcoming the tragedy is based on how you respond. How do you typically handle traumatic experiences?

____

____

____

____

____

113. Would you consider yourself a jealous person? How does jealousy affect your communication, attitude and interaction within your overall character in the relationship?

____

____

____

____

____

114. How do you feel about your spouse going out for a social evening without you? How often would you feel is acceptable?

____

____

____

____

115. One loves to travel, the other does not, are you comfortable with your partner traveling on guy trips or girl trips without you?

____

____

____

____

____

116. How important is the weight and physical appearance of your mate to you over the long term of your relationship?

____

____

____

____

____

117. How would you respond to your spouse if you feel their form of discipline is abusive?

____

____

____

____

____

____

118. How do you feel about your spouse making personal large purchases in your name and on your credit?

____

____

____

____

____

119. What is your credit score?

____

____

____

____

____

120. Mental illness is a part of our lives. Do you believe that you will be able to stand by your partner that is diagnosed with a mental illness like schizophrenia or bipolar, and refuses medication?

____

____

____

____

____

____

121. Holidays are coming, what is your preference? A quiet time at home with your immediate family, a big gathering at your home with an open invite, or house hopping to various family and friends gathering?

____

____

____

____

____

123. The tax season could become a very stressful season in a marriage, there are various ways to file, some will allow greater returns than others, but may not be the most ethical. How would you prefer to file taxes as a married couple? Do you believe it's ok to have a close friend of the opposite sex?

____

____

____

____

____

____

____

____

124. Do you believe it's ok to maintain a relationship with your ex?

____

____

____

____

____

125. If your marriage will create a blended family, how important is it for you to have a relationship with your spouse's ex?

____

____

____

____

____

126. In a blended family, do you believe the non-organic parent should be allowed to physically discipline the child(ren) from the EX-partner?

____

____

____

____

____

127. Marriage comes with a lot of stress; loss of employment or income can happen. How well do you handle stress, for example, having to support the household as a result of your spouse losing their job, and your source of income is not enough?

____

____

____

____

____

128. How do u handle a partner that has an addiction to gambling, porn, or becomes a pedophile or a thief?

____

____

____

____

____

129. Unfortunately, divorce is a part of life which often times creates blended families. As a result, interactions with an EX may be necessary for the sake of the children. How would you respond with a difficult EX that creates chaos in the process?

____

____

130. Do you or your mate have to pay child support or alimony as a result of a previous relationship? If so, do you feel this should be a joint expense or an expense for the person responsible for the child support?

131. If your potential partner already has children from a previous relationship and they opted to live with you, would you be in agreement? Explain why or why not?

132. What are your thoughts on allowing your former partner to have keys or access to your home just in case an emergency? Do you believe your ex should be a beneficiary of your life insurance policy if you have children together?

____

____

____

____

____

____

133. You have a blended family, your spouse and his/or ex have a decent co-parenting relationship, your partner's ex is a very good cook and send your partner a plate or their favorite dessert for the Holidays, there is no interaction with the ex directly, only through the children. Are you ok with this?

____

____

____

____

____

____

____

134. In a blended family with smaller children from the previous relationship, are you comfortable with your spouse buying gifts "from the children" to give to your EX?

____

____

____

____

____

135. Does Size Matter, if so, what's enough for you?

____

____

____

____

____

____

136. How easily are you to ejaculate, (On demand or requires a lot of work)?

____

____

____

____

____

____

137. Are you a sensual person?

138. Do you think it's important to shower before having sex?

139. Your partner has gained weight over the years, you are not physically or sexually attracted to them at this current weight. Do you tell them or just accept it and fake it?

140. What are your thoughts about having an open relationship with other couples (swinging)?

141. How do you feel about having an open marriage?

142. How do you feel about the usage of sex toys with your partner?

143. How important is affection and non-verbal communication to you?

144. What is your sexual fantasy?

145. Do you like public display of affection?

146. How do you think you would respond to being informed by your partner that they have been infected by an STD?

147. What is your favorite time of day to have sex? If your partner enjoys morning sex, and you are not a morning person, how do you respond?

____

____

____

____

____

____

148. The relationship is not going well, you do not desire to have sex with your partner, however, you do not want to separate, your partner has a sexual appetite and still have needs, they go outside of the marriage to get them met. Who's to blame?

____

____

____

____

____

IDENTIFYING
Compromise

Disagreement

____

____

____

____

____

____

____

Compromise

____

____

____

____

____

____

____

____

Disagreement

Compromise

Disagreement

____

____

____

____

____

____

____

____

Compromise

____

____

____

____

____

____

We hereby agree to disagree and adhere to the above written compromise in the areas of disagreement.

____________________	____________________
Signature	Signature

CONCLUSION

Marriage is a very important component of society. It gives the perfect picture as to what society, community, and life is built upon. Nevertheless, it can be a very painful experience for all parties involved when and if the marriage does not work out. Though love becomes the foundation by which marriage is built, there are various factors that directly affect the longevity and viability of the relationship that this love brings. In addition, in our society there are other elements that contribute to a couple getting married, such as the unplanned birth of a child or the influence of peers. Whatever the reason for making such a life changing decision, this decision should not be taken lightly and all factors should be carefully assessed.

Ultimately, time will be the greatest teacher of compatibility in the relationship. As a result, it is highly recommended that you do not enter into marriage anxiously, rather, you should allow time to yield experiences, circumstances, and situations that are sure to bring out the true essence of the personality, character, and mindset of your partner. Furthermore, please understand — what you see is truly what you get. Sometimes love blinds us and prohibits our ability to honestly deal with the behavior of our loved ones, as a result, we look to make excuses for certain actions we would otherwise not tolerate. It is important to understand, that life's journey will eventually reveal and teach us who we really are as individuals, do not allow love to hinder your ability to pass the test. Pay close attention to the sequence of events that happens throughout the dating process. Examine how your partner handles various scenarios, what makes him/her angry? How does he/she respond to anger? How does they response make you feel? Look at who gives more into the relationship now, usually, that person will be the giver throughout the marriage. How do you feel about giving more than you receive or vice versa?

One can go on and on about the difficulties of marriage, the point is to encourage you to kiss with your eyes closed if you will, but before you say I do, proceed with your eyes wide open. Statistics show a decrease in divorce with marriages that had extensive premarital counseling. Understand that feelings will change and desires will shift as you and your partner grow and mature. However, having a good foundation of compatibility will assist in the changes that occur, minimizing the negative impact on the viability of the marriage. The more you know about an individual, and the more you engage in dialogue, the more you empower yourself to make the best decision for the rest of your life. After answering and discussing the previous 149 questions before you say, "I do," after assessing your disagreements and defining your compromise, after charting your score in determining compatibility, I hope you find that you are not only in love, but that you have found a compatible mate.

As we conclude together, please find the final two questions that I believe are paramount to your happily ever after…

Final Questions

150: What do you like the least about your partner? If they never changed, would you still be willing to say I DO?

151: Will you marry me?

CONGRATULATIONS!

Above all I wish that you will prosper and

be in health even as thy soul prospers.

PROSPER!

NOTES

For more information or to contact Dan D. Johnson,

please write, call, or e-mail:

Dan D. Johnson

430 E. 162nd St., Suite 531

South Holland, IL 60473

www.danjohnsonworldwide.com

For testimonials or questions email Dan Personally

at **empoweredbydan@gmail.com**

Follow me @DanDJohnson on